This igloo book belongs to:

....

igloobooks

Published in 2012
by Igloo Books Ltd
Cottage Farm
Sywell
NN6 0BJ
www.igloobooks.com

SHE001 1012
2 4 6 8 10 9 7 5 3 1
ISBN 978-0-85780-855-4

Printed and manufactured in China

My Treasury of Nursery Rhymes

igloobooks

Contents

MARY HAD A LITTLE LAMB

Mary had a little lamb,
Whose fleece was white as snow.
And everywhere that Mary went,
The lamb was sure to go.

He followed her to school one day,
That was against the rule.
It made the children laugh and play,
To see a lamb at school.

And so the teacher turned it out,
But still it lingered near.
And waited patiently about,
'Til Mary did appear.

"Why does the lamb love Mary so?"
The eager children cry.
"Why, Mary loves the lamb, you know,"
The teacher did reply.

6

Jack And Jill

Jack and Jill went up the hill,
To fetch a pail of water.
Jack fell down and broke his crown,
And Jill came tumbling after.

Up got Jack, and home did trot,
As fast as he could caper.
He went to bed and bound his head,
With vinegar and brown paper.

HEY DIDDLE DIDDLE

Hey diddle, diddle,
The cat and the fiddle,
The cow jumped over the moon.

The little dog laughed,
To see such fun,
And the dish ran away,
With the spoon!

OLD MACDONALD

Old MacDonald had a farm, E-I-E-I-O.
And on that farm he had some ducks, E-I-E-I-O.
With a **quack, quack** here and a **quack, quack** there,
Here a **quack**, there a **quack**, everywhere a **quack, quack**.
Old MacDonald had a farm, E-I-E-I-O.

Old MacDonald had a farm, E-I-E-I-O.
And on that farm he had some cows, E-I-E-I-O.
With a **moo, moo** here and a **moo, moo** there,
Here a **moo**, there a **moo**, everywhere a **moo, moo**.
Old MacDonald had a farm, E-I-E-I-O.

Old MacDonald had a farm, E-I-E-I-O.
And on that farm he had some sheep, E-I-E-I-O.
With a **baa, baa** here and a **baa, baa** there,
Here a **baa**, there a **baa**, everywhere a **baa, baa**.
Old MacDonald had a farm, E-I-E-I-O.

Old MacDonald had a farm, E-I-E-I-O.
And on that farm he had some pigs, E-I-E-I-O.
With a **snort, snort** here and a **snort, snort** there,
Here a **snort**, there a **snort**, everywhere a **snort, snort**.
Old MacDonald had a farm, E-I-E-I-O.

Baa, Baa, Black Sheep

Baa, baa, black sheep,
Have you any wool?
Yes, sir, yes, sir,
Three bags full.
One for the master,
And one for the dame,
And one for the little boy,
Who lives down the lane.

LITTLE JACK HORNER

Little Jack Horner sat in the corner,
Eating a Christmas pie.
He put in his thumb,
And pulled out a plum,
And said, "What a good boy am I!"

POLLY PUT THE KETTLE ON

Polly put the kettle on,
Polly put the kettle on,
Polly put the kettle on,
We'll all have tea.

Sukey take it off again,
Sukey take it off again,
Sukey take it off again,
They've all gone away.

12

OLD MOTHER HUBBARD

Old Mother Hubbard,
Went to the cupboard,
To give her poor dog a bone.
But when she got there,
The cupboard was bare,
And so the poor dog had none.

I'M A LITTLE TEAPOT

I'm a little teapot, short and stout.
Here is my handle, here is my spout.
When I get all steamed up, hear me shout,
Tip me over and pour me out.

THE FARMER'S IN HIS DEN

The farmer's in his den,
The farmer's in his den,
E-I-E-I-O, the farmer's in his den.

The farmer wants a wife,
The farmer wants a wife,
E-I-E-I-O, the farmer wants a wife.

The wife wants a child,
The wife wants a child,
E-I-E-I-O, the wife wants a child.

The child wants a nurse,
The child wants a nurse,
E-I-E-I-O, the child wants a nurse.

The nurse wants a dog,
The nurse wants a dog,
E-I-E-I-O, the nurse wants a dog.

The dog wants a bone,
The dog wants a bone,
E-I-E-I-O, the dog wants a bone.

We all pat the bone,
We all pat the bone,
E-I-E-I-O, we all pat the bone.

THE COCK CROWS

The cock crows in the morn,
To tell us to rise,
And he that lies late,
Will never be wise.

For early to bed,
And early to rise,
Is the way to be healthy,
And wealthy and wise.

LITTLE BO-PEEP

Little Bo-Peep has lost her sheep,
And can't tell where to find them.
Leave them alone, and they'll come home,
Bringing their tails behind them.

15

I Had A Little Nut Tree

I had a little nut tree,
Nothing would it bear,
But a silver nutmeg,
And a golden pear.
The King of Spain's daughter,
Came to visit me.
And all for the sake,
Of my little nut tree.

Her dress was made of crimson,
Jet black was her hair.
She asked me for my nut tree,
And my golden pear.
I said, "So fair a princess,
Never did I see.
I'll give you all the fruit,
From my little nut tree."

The Grand Old Duke Of York

The grand old Duke of York,
He had ten thousand men.
He marched them up to the top of the hill,
And he marched them down again.

And when they were up, they were up,
And when they were down, they were down,
And when they were only halfway up,
They were neither up nor down!

17

Star Light, Star Bright

Star light, star bright,
The first star I see tonight,
I wish I may, I wish I might,
Have the wish I wish tonight.

Sleep, Baby, Sleep

Sleep, baby, sleep,
Your father tends the sheep,
Your mother shakes the dreamland tree,
And from it fall sweet dreams for thee.
Sleep, baby, sleep.
Sleep, baby, sleep.

18

THE MAN IN THE MOON

The man in the moon came tumbling down,
And asked the way to Norwich.
He went by the south, and burnt his mouth,
With eating cold pease porridge.

EARLY TO BED

Early to bed,
Early to rise.
Makes little Johnny,
Wealthy and wise.

19

Rain, Rain, Go Away

Rain, rain, go away,
Come again another day,
Little Johnny wants to play.

Georgie Porgie

Georgie Porgie, pudding and pie,
Kissed the girls and made them cry.
When the boys came out to play,
Georgie Porgie ran away.

Kookaburra

Kookaburra sits on an old gum tree,
Merry, merry king of the bush is he.
Laugh, kookaburra, laugh, kookaburra,
Gay your life must be.

A Tisket, A Tasket

A tisket, a tasket,
A green and yellow basket.
I wrote a letter to my love,
But on the way I dropped it.
I dropped it, I dropped it,
And, on the way I dropped it.
A little boy picked it up,
And put it in his pocket.

23

THE OWL AND THE PUSSYCAT

The owl and the pussycat went to sea,
In a beautiful pea-green boat.
They took some honey, and plenty of money,
Wrapped up in a five-pound note.

The owl looked up to the stars above,
And sang to a small guitar.
"O lovely pussy, O pussy my love,
What a beautiful pussy you are, you are!
What a beautiful pussy you are!"

Pussy said to the owl, "You elegant fowl,
How charmingly sweet you sing!
Oh! Let us be married, too long we have tarried,
But what shall we do for a ring?"

They sailed away, for a year and a day,
To the land where the bong-tree grows.
And there in a wood a piggy-wig stood,
With a ring at the end of his nose, his nose,
With a ring at the end of his nose.

"Dear pig, are you willing to sell for one shilling,
Your ring?" Said the piggy, "I will."
So they took it away and were married next day,
By the turkey who lives on the hill.

They dined on mince and slices of quince,
Which they ate with a runcible spoon.
And hand in hand on the edge of the sand,
They danced by the light of the moon, the moon,
They danced by the light of the moon.

FIVE LITTLE DUCKS

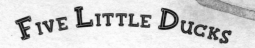

Five little ducks
Went out one day,
Over the hill and far away.
Mother duck said,
"Quack, quack, quack, quack."
But only four little ducks came back.

Four little ducks
Went out one day,
Over the hill and far away.
Mother duck said,
"Quack, quack, quack, quack."
But only three little ducks came back.

Three little ducks
Went out one day,
Over the hill and far away.
Mother duck said,
"Quack, quack, quack, quack."
But only two little ducks came back.

Two little ducks
Went out one day,
Over the hill and far away.
Mother duck said,
"Quack, quack, quack, quack."
But only one little duck came back.

Row, Row, Row Your Boat

Row, row, row your boat,
Gently down the stream.
Merrily, merrily, merrily,
Life is but a dream.

Row, row, row your boat,
Gently down the stream.
If you see a crocodile,
Don't forget to scream.

One little duck
Went out one day,
Over the hill and far away.
Mother duck said,
"Quack, quack, quack, quack."
And all of the five little ducks came back.

27

To Market

To market, to market, to buy a fat pig,
Home again, home again, jiggety jig.

To market, to market, to buy a fat hog,
Home again, home again, jiggety jog.

To market, to market, to buy a plum bun,
Home again, home again, market is done.

THE MUFFIN MAN

Oh do you know the Muffin Man,
The Muffin Man,
The Muffin Man?
Do you know the Muffin Man,
That lives in Drury Lane?

Oh yes I know the Muffin Man,
The Muffin Man,
The Muffin Man.
Yes I know the Muffin Man,
That lives in Drury Lane.

HOT-CROSS BUNS

Hot-cross buns, hot-cross buns!
One a-penny, two a-penny,
Hot-cross buns!

29

Dance To Your Daddy

Dance to your daddy,
My bonnie laddy,
Dance to your daddy,
My bonnie lamb.

You shall get a fishy,
In a little dishy,
You shall have a fishy,
When the boat comes in.

You shall get a coatie,
And a pair of breeches,
And you'll get an eggy,
And a bit of ham.

THE BIG SHIP SAILS

The big ship sails,
On the alley, alley oh.
The alley, alley oh.
The big ship sails,
On the alley, alley oh,
On the last day of December.

31

PAT-A-CAKE

Pat-a-cake, pat-a-cake,
Baker's man.
Bake me a cake,
As fast as you can.
Roll it, and poke it,
And mark it with B.
And throw it in the oven,
For baby and me.

OLD KING COLE

Old King Cole,
Was a merry old soul,
And a merry old soul was he.

He called for his pipe,
And he called for his bowl,
And he called for his fiddlers three!

And every fiddler, he had a fine fiddle,
And a very fine fiddle had he.
"Twee tweedle dee, tweedle dee,"
Went the fiddlers three.

Oh, there's none so rare,
As can compare,
With King Cole and his fiddlers three.

THE QUEEN OF HEARTS

The Queen of Hearts,
She made some tarts,
All on a summer's day.

The Knave of Hearts,
He stole those tarts,
And took them clean away.

The King of Hearts,
Called for the tarts,
And beat the Knave full sore.

The Knave of Hearts,
Brought back the tarts,
And vowed he'd steal no more.

HUSH-A-BYE

Hush-a-bye, baby, on the tree top,
When the wind blows the cradle will rock,
When the bough breaks the cradle will fall,
Down will come baby, cradle and all.

THE APPLE TREE

Here is the tree with leaves so green,
Here are the apples that hang between.
When the wind blows, the apples fall,
Here is a basket to gather them all.

A Swarm Of Bees

A swarm of bees in May,
Is worth a load of hay.
A swarm of bees in June,
Is worth a silver spoon.
A swarm of bees in July,
Is not worth a fly.

Miss Muffet

Little Miss Muffet,
Sat on a tuffet,
Eating her curds and whey.
There came a big spider,
Who sat down beside her,
And frightened Miss Muffet away.

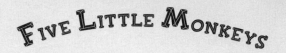

Five Little Monkeys

Five little monkeys jumping on the bed,
One fell off and bumped his head.
Mummy called the doctor and the doctor said,
"No more monkeys jumping on the bed!"

Four little monkeys jumping on the bed,
One fell off and bumped his head.
Mummy called the doctor and the doctor said,
"No more monkeys jumping on the bed!"

Three little monkeys jumping on the bed,
One fell off and bumped his head.
Mummy called the doctor and the doctor said,
"No more monkeys jumping on the bed!"

Two little monkeys jumping on the bed,
One fell off and bumped his head.
Mummy called the doctor and the doctor said,
"No more monkeys jumping on the bed!"

One little monkey jumping on the bed,
He fell off and bumped his head.
Mummy called the doctor and the doctor said,
"No more monkeys jumping on the bed!"

No little monkeys jumping on the bed,
None fell off and bumped their head.
Mummy called the doctor and the doctor said,
"That's what you get for jumping on the bed!"

THE MULBERRY BUSH

Here we go round the mulberry bush,
The mulberry bush, the mulberry bush.
Here we go round the mulberry bush,
So early in the morning.

MARY, MARY, QUITE CONTRARY

Mary, Mary quite contrary,
How does your garden grow?
With silver bells and cockle shells,
And pretty maids all in a row.

38

ROUND AND ROUND THE GARDEN

Round and round the garden,
Like a teddy bear.
One step, two step,
Tickle you under there.

TWO LITTLE DICKY BIRDS

Two little dicky birds,
Sat upon a wall.
One named Peter,
The other named Paul.
Fly away, Peter,
Fly away, Paul.
Come back, Peter,
Come back, Paul.

39

Sing A Song Of Sixpence

Sing a song of sixpence,
A pocket full of rye.
Four-and-twenty blackbirds,
Baked in a pie!

When the pie was opened,
The birds began to sing.
Wasn't that a dainty dish,
To set before the king?

The king was in his counting-house,
Counting out his money.
The queen was in the parlor,
Eating bread and honey.

The maid was in the garden,
Hanging out the clothes.
When down came a blackbird,
And pecked off her nose.

Humpty Dumpty

Humpty Dumpty sat on a wall.
Humpty Dumpty had a great fall.
All the king's horses and all the king's men,
Couldn't put Humpty together again.

The Lion And The Unicorn

The lion and the unicorn,
Were fighting for the crown.
The lion chased the unicorn,
All about the town.

Some gave them white bread,
And some gave them brown.
Some gave them plum cake,
And sent them out of town.

41

I See The Moon

I see the moon,
And the moon sees me.
God bless the moon,
And God bless me.

Wee Willie Winkie

Wee Willie Winkie runs through the town,
Upstairs and downstairs, in his nightgown.
Tapping at the window, crying through the lock,
"Are the children in their beds,
Now it's eight o'clock?"

42

BOYS AND GIRLS, COME OUT TO PLAY

Girls and boys, come out to play,
The moon does shine as bright as day.
Leave your supper, and leave your sleep,
And come with your play fellows into the street.
Come with a whoop, come with a call,
Come with a good will or not at all.
Up the ladder and down the wall,
A halfpenny roll will serve us all.
You find milk, and I'll find flour,
And we'll have a pudding,
In half an hour.

43

Oranges And Lemons

"Oranges and lemons," say the bells of St. Clement's.
"You owe me five farthings," say the bells of St. Martin's.
"When will you pay me?" say the bells of Old Bailey.
"When I grow rich," say the bells of Shoreditch.
"When will that be?" say the bells of Stepney.
"I do not know," says the great bell at Bow.
"Here comes a candle to light you to bed.
Here comes a chopper to chop off your head.
Chip chop chip chop - the last man's dead."

Yankee Doodle

Yankee Doodle went to town,
A-riding on a pony.
He stuck a feather in his hat,
And called it macaroni.

Yankee Doodle, keep it up,
Yankee Doodle dandy.
Mind the music and the step,
And with the girls be handy.

There were ten in a bed and the little one said,
"Roll over! Roll over!"
So they all rolled over and one fell out.

There were nine in a bed and the little one said,
"Roll over! Roll over!"
So they all rolled over and one fell out.

There were eight in a bed and the little one said,
"Roll over! Roll over!"
So they all rolled over and one fell out.

There were seven in a bed and the little one said,
"Roll over! Roll over!"
So they all rolled over and one fell out.

There were six in a bed and the little one said,
"Roll over! Roll over!"
So they all rolled over and one fell out.

There were five in a bed and the little one said,
"Roll over! Roll over!"
So they all rolled over and one fell out.

There were four in a bed and the little one said,
"Roll over! Roll over!"
So they all rolled over and one fell out.

There were three in a bed and the little one said,
"Roll over! Roll over!"
So they all rolled over and one fell out.

There were two in a bed and the little one said,
"Roll over! Roll over!"
So they all rolled over and one fell out.

There was one in a bed and the little one said,
"Good night!"

COME TO THE WINDO

Come to the window,
My baby, with me,
And look at the stars,
That shine on the sea!

There are two little stars,
That play bo-peep.
With two little fishes,
Far down in the deep.

And two little frogs,
Cry "Neap, neap, neap."
I see a dear baby,
That should be asleep.

DIDDLE DIDDLE DUMPLING

Diddle diddle dumpling, my son John,
Went to bed with his breeches on.
One stocking off, and one stocking on,
Diddle diddle dumpling, my son John.

THE MOON

The moon is round,
As round can be.
Two eyes, a nose and a mouth,
Like me!

TWINKLE, TWINKLE, LITTLE STAR

Twinkle, twinkle, little star,
How I wonder what you are.
Up above the world so high,
Like a diamond in the sky.
Twinkle, twinkle, little star,
How I wonder what you are.

JACK SPRAT

Jack Sprat could eat no fat,
His wife could eat no lean.
And so between them both, you see,
They licked the platter clean.

RING-A-RING O'ROSES

Ring-a-ring o'roses,
A pocket full of posies,
Atishoo! Atishoo!
We all fall down.

SEE-SAW, MARGERY DAW

See-saw, Margery Daw,
Jacky shall have a new master.
He shall have but a penny a day,
Because he can't work any faster.

53

I Saw Three Ships

I saw three ships come sailing by,
Come sailing by, come sailing by,
I saw three ships come sailing by,
On New Year's Day in the morning.

And what do you think was in them then,
Was in them then, was in them then?
And what do you think was in them then,
On New Year's Day in the morning.

Three pretty girls were in them then,
Were in them then, were in them then,
Three pretty girls were in them then,
On New Year's Day in the morning.

One could whistle, and one could sing,
And one could play the violin,
Such joy there was at my wedding,
On New Year's Day in the morning.

BOBBY SHAFTOE

Bobby Shaftoe went to sea,
Silver buckles on his knee.
He'll come back and marry me,
Pretty Bobby Shaftoe.

Bobby Shaftoe's fine and fair,
Combing down his auburn hair.
He's my friend for ever more,
Pretty Bobby Shaftoe.

RUB-A-DUB

Rub-a-dub-dub,
Three men in a tub,
And who do you think they be?
The butcher, the baker,
The candlestick maker.
They all sailed out to sea.

55

ONE, TWO, BUCKLE MY SHOE

One, two,
Buckle my shoe.

Three, four,
Knock at the door.

Five, six,
Pick up sticks.

Seven, eight,
Lay them straight.

Nine, ten,
A good, fat hen.

Eleven, twelve,
Dig and delve.

Thirteen, fourteen,
Maids a-courting.

Fifteen, sixteen,
Maids in the kitchen.

Seventeen, eighteen,
Maids a-waiting.

Nineteen, twenty,
My plate's empty.

Hickory Dickory Dock

Hickory dickory dock,
The mouse ran up the clock.
The clock struck one,
The mouse ran down,
Hickory dickory dock.

Once I Saw A Little Bird

Once I saw a little bird,
Go hop, hop, hop.
So I cried, little bird,
"Will you stop, stop, stop?"
And I was going to the window,
To say, "How do you do?"
When he shook his little tail,
And away he flew.

59

A Needle And Thread

Old Mother Twitchett had but one eye,
And a long tail which she let fly,
And every time she went through a gap,
A bit of her tail she left in a trap.

There Was An Old Woman

There was an old woman,
Who lived in a shoe.
She had so many children,
She didn't know what to do.
She gave them some broth,
Without any bread.
She said, "Goodnight children",
And sent them to bed.

I'm A Dingly Dangly Scarecrow

I'm a dingly, dangly scarecrow,
With a flippy, floppy hat.
I can shake my hands like this,
I can shake my feet like that.

THE NORTH WIND DOTH BLOW

The north wind doth blow,
And we shall have snow,
And what will poor robin do then,
Poor thing?
He'll sit in a barn,
And keep himself warm,
And hide his head under his wing,
Poor thing!

JACK-A-NORY

I'll tell you a story about Jack-a-Nory,
And now my story's told.
I'll tell you another,
About Jack and his brother,
And now my story's done.